innovations in machinery, particularly the beam engines for pumping and winding, and crushing ores.

Tin was smelted in Cornwall, but the copper ore was shipped to smelters in South Wales, the small schooners returning with coal for the engines on the mines. Mineral railways to ports on the coast were part of this two-way trade. This was all at a high price in terms of the miners' health, for they often worked in appaling conditions at a great depth, reached every day by climbing up and down long ladders in the dark.

After the mid-nineteenth century, when foreign competition depressed the price of copper and then tin, hundreds of mines were hastily abandoned or 'knacked' and many of the miners and their families were forced to emigrate to mineral fields around the world. The legacy is a unique landscape studded with empty engine houses, one which is immediately recognisable as Cornish and a reminder that many parts of this rural county were once bustling with industry.

Crowns Shaft, Botallack M.J.M.

Cornwall's mineral wealth lies in its geology. The spine of the peninsula is formed by granite uplands from Dartmoor (Devon) westwards through Bodmin Moor, Hensbarrow, Carnmenellis, and West Penwith, with the Isles of Scilly beyond. Lesser outcrops of granite associated with mining include Carn Brea, Carn Marth, Castle-an-Dinas, Hingston Down, Kit Hill, St Agnes and Tregonning. These were intruded as molten bosses beneath older rocks about 280 million years ago, and have been revealed by subsequent erosion. Around each granite margin is the metamorphic aureole, a ring of baked rocks known locally as killas. It is here that the richest mining districts of Cornwall are found.

During a late cooling stage of the molten granite, fissures opened up into which passed mineralising fluids combined with circulating water which cooled to form mineral lodes. Normally the vertical order of deposition of minerals upwards is tin, copper, zinc lead and iron. Unwanted 'gangue' minerals in the lodes include tourmaline, quartz, fluorspar and calcite. The tin and copper lodes

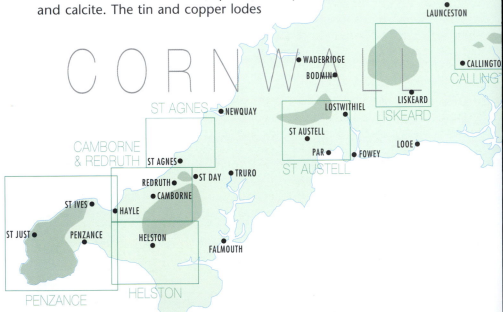

Cornwall showing the location of the mining districts

extend from the granite out into the killas and trend generally east-west throughout the county. Lead, zinc and iron were deposited at lower temperatures in a final stage in mainly north-south lodes (crosscourses) which are found further away from the granite. Unlike coal seams, which were laid down horizontally in sedimentary rocks, the lodes tend to be near-vertical. Sometimes they dip at a lesser angle, the most important being the Great Flat Lode which was worked profitably by several mines to the south of Carn Brea. They may also be displaced by faulting. A mass of ore veinlets is known as a stockwork, and was worked by opencast methods such as at Mulberry and Wheal Prosper near Lanivet.

ORES

Tin ore is cassiterite, a dark black-brown mineral, found in lodes or deposited in valley gravels. After treatment, this 'black tin' might be about 65% pure tin. The commonest copper ore to be mined was chalcopyrite, also known as copper pyrites or 'yellow copper ore'. The grey chalcocite was also important at some mines, while azurite, malachite, melaconite and cuprite were also worked. Ores contained only 6 to 12% copper, so mining was on a much larger scale than for tin. Arsenopyrite, or mispickle, contains up to 46% arsenic, and was a by-product of tin and copper mines. Later in the nineteenth century it was an important earner when metal prices slumped. Galena is the ore for lead, yielding up to 75% metal, while the zinc ore was blende or black jack, with up to 45% metal content. Silver has been mostly recovered from lead ores, the chief districts being around St Agnes and Liskeard.

The main commercial iron ores have been limonite, siderite and haematite. Workings were never very deep for these low valued ores. Some mines were productive in iron pyrites, or mundic, used for making sulphuric acid. Wolfram is found near the top of the tin zone. It is difficult to separate from the tin, but is valued as a source of tungsten for hardening steel. Some mines have been worked for it alone, the most notable being at Castle-an-Dinas. Other minerals worked in a small way include antimony and manganese. Uranium (pitchblende) was produced at Wheal Trenwith near St Ives and South Terras near St Austell. Gold has been found in mines, but the only real quantities have been recovered from alluvial tin works.

Botallack Count House P.S.

TIN

The occurrence of tin is much rarer than other metals such as copper or iron, and although only a small amount was added to copper to make bronze, its scarcity must have made Cornwall an important source in prehistoric Britain and Europe. There is no proof that Bronze Age peoples worked tin here, but it is perhaps no coincidence that their abundant villages and stone circles are close to where tin is later known to have been exploited on the moors of Bodmin Moor, Dartmoor and West Penwith.

The earliest tin workings were not mines but streamworks. Past erosion of lodes had removed tin stones (cassiterite), sorted and deposited them in valley gravels where they could be worked relatively easily by washing away the lighter material. As methods improved over the centuries, increasingly poorer deposits could be worked, so many valley floors have been turned over time and time again, often destroying any earlier evidence.

Wheal Ellen, with Tywarnhayle Mine in the background P.S.

It is known that tin was traded with the Mediterranean world in Iron Age times. In the first century BC, Diodorus Siculus described how the people of Belerion (Land's End) prepared the tin, carefully working the ground containing 'earthy veins, the produce of which is ground down, smelted and purified.' This seems to be a clear reference to tin-streaming. The industry was well established, with the locals trading their tin with merchants on an island named Ictis, generally considered to be St Michael's Mount, although there are other contenders as far east as the Isle of Wight. A fine ingot from

Tin ingot dredged up from St Mawes harbour.

this period has been dredged from St Mawes harbour and is now in the Royal Cornwall Museum at Truro. The Romans took an interest in Cornish tin after their Spanish source failed in the third century AD, and an ingot from Carnanton is said to have been marked with a Roman stamp.

In medieval times streamworks were still abundant, but there were shallow workings along some lodes. Dartmoor became the greatest tin producer in Europe in the Middle Ages, but the easily worked streams soon ran out and Cornwall regained its pre-eminence. Uses of tin at this time included cannons and bells of bronze (with copper), although articles of pewter (with lead) were still luxuries.

The tin industries of Cornwall and Devon were regulated by the ancient Stannaries, which held jurisdiction over large areas, similar to the lead mining districts of the Mendips and Peak District. The first known charter of 1201 confirmed the tinners' right of 'bounding' to search and dig for tin on unenclosed common land and to divert any stream for their use. There were Stannary Courts and a Parliament which met periodically to pass and amend the law. Heavy penalties were imposed on offenders by the courts and Lydford, on the edge of Dartmoor, still has the ruins of a formidable gaol. Cornwall's was at Lostwithiel.

An engraving of Dolcoath Mine in about 1831. It clearly shows surface dressing of the copper ores and the capstan and sheer legs for the shaftwork COLLECTION M.J.M.

DOLCOATH COPPER MINE, CAMBORNE, CORNWALL.

A modern mine - Wheal Jane, showing Clemow's and No. 2 Shafts, now abandoned M.J.M.

The system of coinage took place at the towns of Liskeard, Lostwithiel, Helston and Truro, with Penzance added in 1663. The first two were later replaced by Calstock, Hayle and St Austell. Each ingot was weighed to assess the duty to be paid to the Duke of Cornwall and a corner, or 'coign', was struck off to be assayed for quality. The tin block was stamped with the Duchy seal and only then could it be sold. Coinage ceased in 1838 and the courts in 1896, although the stannary charters have never been repealed.

Stream tin and shallow mining could not meet increasing demand, but the main obstacle to deep mining was the removal of water. Pumps worked by waterwheels had their limitations, so it was timely that the eighteenth century saw the application of steam power to pumping. The story of these developments in Cornwall was linked more closely with the rapid rise of copper mining. First came the beam engines of Newcomen and Watt, developed further by Cornish engineers like Richard Trevithick and Arthur Woolf. The Cornish beam engine reached perfection in the nineteenth century, initially for pumping, and then for winding and ore crushing.

Early tin mines of importance were Great Work and Wheal Vor, recorded as active in the fifteenth century. The greatest tin mine was Dolcoath at Camborne, successful first for copper, but when this started to fail in the 1840s the mine was able to turn to deep tin, something which occurred at many other mines. This celebrated mine became a major tin producer by the end of the nineteenth century, and reached a depth of 550 fathoms (3,300 feet), the deepest of any Cornish mine. It closed in 1921, after over a century of continuous working. Camborne-Redruth was the major tin mining district, but other important districts were Callington (Kit Hill-Gunnislake), Helston (around Godolphin Hill and Wendron), Liskeard (Phoenix mines), Penzance (around St Just and St Ives), and St Agnes.

The earliest smelting of stream tin took place using charcoal in small water-powered blowing houses, of which the best examples can be seen today on Dartmoor. The product was known as 'grain tin.' All Cornish tin was smelted at home. Smelting houses were set up in most districts in the eighteenth and nineteenth centuries, producing 'white tin' in reverberatory furnaces. Notable houses were Chyandour at Penzance, Mellanear at Hayle, and Calenick near Truro, a town which had three other works. Wheal Vor produced enough tin to have its own works for a short period. The Cornish Tin Smelting Co.'s works at Seleggan near Redruth was the last to close, in 1931.

Tin blocks awaiting shipment were once a common sight on the quays at Truro and Penzance. Uses of tin in the nineteenth century included bronze, solder, pewter and the tin plate industry, already established in South Wales.

Mining has always been a risky business, subject to fluctuations in the base metal price. Cornish tin suffered set-backs as the price fell from the 1860s, due first to the American Civil War. There was some revival, but the fate of the tin mines was sealed after 1873. The discovery of tin in Australia coincided with renewed output from the Malayan alluvial workings, and tin prices fell rapidly. At the turn of the century, Bolivian tin entered the market.

A TIN MINE, CORNWALL.

A view of the extensive dressing works of the East Pool and Agar Mines in the Tolvadden Valley. Albeit not so extensive such scenes were typical of the many areas of Cornwall when mining was at its height CORNISH STUDIES LIBRARY

Many important mines closed in the 1890s, so that by 1900 only a handful were left. A rapid recovery in the tin price led to a revival of mining around 1906, but the Great War soon ended that. Following the war there was a severe slump in the 1920s, but the Cornish tin industry did not give up the struggle and die.

Only South Crofty and Geevor had survived this unhappy period, when rising world tin prices in the 1960s led to renewed interest. Prospecting and development work took place around the county, and when Wheal Jane began production in 1971 it was the first major new tin mine for over half a century. Within three years the output of Cornish tin was doubled and copper and zinc were produced too. There were other new mines, at nearby Mount Wellington and Pendarves near Camborne, and the small Wheal Concorde tin mine was started near Blackwater. Tin reached £10,430 per tonne before the market collapsed in October 1985. South Crofty, Geevor and Wheal Jane struggled on for a while, but today they have all closed.

COPPER

Although tin is popularly associated with Cornwall, copper mining was of far greater significance in terms of the size of mines and the quantity produced. Low grade ores meant that much had to be mined to produce one ton of copper metal.

While the tin industry had existed for many years, it is uncertain when copper was first worked. It was not until 1579 that any serious attempt was made to exploit Cornwall's copper ores, when Thomas Smyth was granted a lease to explore for copper in Devon and Cornwall, placing one Ulricke Frosse as 'ovseer of ye minerall woorkes at Trewoorth, near unto Perin Sandes'. About a century later, the art of smelting copper with coal was perfected, and because of the great amount of coal needed in the processes, smelting works were built on the coal fields. In the 1690s, ore was being shipped to Bristol and Upper Redbrook on the Wye. In 1719, a copper combination of partners from these works contracted to run a group of Cornish mines and buy ores at a fixed price. At about the same time, smelters were established in South Wales at Swansea (which became the leading centre), Llanelli and Neath.

It was during the eighteenth century that copper mining was aided by the engines of Newcomen and Watt, when there were increasing demands for the metal, particularly for the sheathing of ships' hulls. However, Thomas Williams' immensely rich Parys opencast mine on Anglesey brought prices crashing, which severely affected the Cornish mines for a decade from about 1785. Mines closed and the 'ticketings' were suspended for a while. When production on Anglesey fell off the mines were re-opened in Cornwall in a new period of activity.

The smelters had a monopoly disliked in Cornwall, for they could control the price offered for ores at the 'ticketings'. This was a system open to abuse whereby the smelters' agents submitted a price on a slip of paper, the ore going to the highest bidder. Some copper was smelted at Hayle in 1758-1819 by the Cornish Copper Co. The Welsh smelters tried hard to preserve their monopoly against this concern which was hardly a serious rival considering the extra expense of bringing coals to Cornwall.

The greatest copper mining district was around St Day and Gwennap, where the Consolidated and United mines (later joined as Clifford Amalgamated) together produced 924,320 tons of copper ore in 1815-72. This was one of the older districts, along with Camborne-Redruth, where Dolcoath and Carn Brea mines were the major producers. As these mines began to fail with depth, new districts were opened up eastwards. From 1822, Fowey Consols produced nearly 320,000 tons over the next 45

Rule's Shaft, South Caradon Mine P.S.

years, while South Caradon started a mining boom to the north of Liskeard and produced 217,820 tons in 1837-85. Devon Great Consols, the richest copper mine of all, was discovered in 1844 just across the Tamar in Devon. There was a corresponding movement of miners and their families from the west into these new eastern districts.

The tiny harbour at Trevaunance, on the coast below St Agnes, was built especially for the mines but has now been almost destroyed by the sea COLLECTION M.J.M.

Copper ores from Cornwall dominated output from the United Kingdom, making it the largest world producer until the 1840s when it began to be overtaken by Chile. The county yielded 163,958 tons of copper ore in the peak year of 1856, but discoveries of rich ore bodies in the Americas and Australia brought prices down and the Cornish mines began to decline. A decade later this grew to a landslide, with mines closing with hundreds of miners thrown out of work and being forced to emigrate to seek work. The more fortunate mines turned to deep tin as Dolcoath had done earlier, but a great number were exhausted and were abandoned for ever.

The copper ore trade stimulated transport developments in Cornwall. The carriage of vast quantities of ores by mules over poor roads was most unsatisfactory, and mineral railways were built from the mines to the ports for shipment of ores to South Wales. The mines around Camborne-Redruth and St Day were served in both directions - to Portreath on the north coast

The locomotive MINER of the Redruth & Chasewater Railway COLLECTION M.J.M.

by the Portreath Tram Road (1812-c70) and south to Devoran by the Redruth & Chasewater Railway (1826-1915). Branches of the Hayle Railway linked mines to Hayle and gave a second route to Portreath after 1838.

Further east, Par Harbour was begun in 1829 by Joseph Treffry and his Fowey Consols copper mine was connected by two inclines and a canal. The quay at East Looe harbour owes its present form, not to fishing, but largely to the copper mines around Caradon Hill which were served by the Liskeard & Caradon Railway (1844-1916). After 1872, the East Cornwall Mineral Railway connected the mines around Callington to Calstock Quay on the Tamar.

These mineral ports were a scene of great activity, for there was a considerable two-way traffic of ores shipped to South Wales and coal brought in return for the engines on the mines. The 'Welsh Fleet' was a collective name given to the many locally owned sailing vessels which served the trade to and from South Wales. These were mostly two-masted schooners, well suited to the small Cornish ports but subject to the hazards of a passage around a dangerous coast.

LEAD

Tin and copper were not the only metals mined in nineteenth century Cornwall, for appreciable amounts of lead, zinc and other minerals were also produced. These mines were not just confined to the main districts, but were scattered throughout the county. For example, in north Cornwall, few would imagine that there had been a small lead mine beneath King Arthur's Castle at Tintagel, or that the cliff tops between Pentire and Port Quin were once the source of antimony.

The main lead mining districts were astride Liskeard at Herodsfoot and Menheniot, and to the south and east of St Agnes. In the latter district, lead ores from East Wheal Rose represented 55% of Cornwall's peak output of 11,674 tons in 1845. Cornwall was a significant producer of lead until the mid-nineteenth century, but mining declined and collapsed in the 1870s. Some lead ores were relatively rich in silver, notably at East Wheal Rose and West Chiverton in the St Agnes district, and Wheal Mary Ann and Trelawny at Menheniot.

As with tin, lead was smelted in Cornwall. Treffry's fleet of sailing vessels brought ores to the smelter at Par harbour from elsewhere in Cornwall and Devon. Shipping bills show that, for example, ore from East Wheal Rose was shipped via the Gannel at Newquay, while finished lead ingots from the works found their way mainly to London. There was a second lead smelting works at Point, downstream from Devoran, where there was also a tin smelting works.

ZINC

Zinc was usually a by-product of tin, copper and lead mines. Its earlier uses were for brass (with copper) and for zinc sheeting; the zinc galvanising process was developed in the 1840s. The biggest output came from West

Chiverton in the late 1870s, when it prolonged the life of the mine at a time when lead production was declining. Zinc was once again mined in Cornwall for the first time in 50 years at the Wheal Jane tin mine. In 1981, the mine produced a record 10,855 tonnes of concentrates, which were shipped off from the port of Truro.

IRON

Iron ore was mined at several locations, but especially in central Cornwall where mines at Pawton, Restormel, Ruby and along the Great Perran Iron Lode were among the most productive. Iron prices, never high, fluctuated wildly from year to year, with a corresponding effect on output. Nevertheless, the prospects for working the Perran lode were considered good enough for the formation of the short-lived Cornwall Minerals Railway in 1873, to improve railway and shipping facilities for a fleet of steam ships at Fowey.

WOLFRAM

Wolfram is usually found with tin, but Castle-an-Dinas Mine worked for it alone. The mineral found little use until tungsten alloys were developed in the second half of the nineteenth century, and by 1910 tungsten lamp filaments were almost universal. Wolfram became strategically important in both world wars, and Hawkswood Mine on Bodmin Moor was opened for a few years in the 1950s, encouraged by high prices created by the Korean war.

ARSENIC

Arsenic was an impurity in tin ores and was removed by calcining. Later

it became important and was sought by the miners, the chief ore being arsenical pyrite. It was calcined and collected in great labyrinthine flues ('lambreths') in many districts. The waste poisonous fumes were carried away by tall stacks which were a major feature in the mining landscape.

Robinsons Shaft, at South Crofty. The engine house contains the preserved 80-inch pumping engine P.S.

The names of Cornish mines make a fascinating study. 'Wheal' is a common prefix and is said to be a corruption of the Cornish huel for a mine working. 'Bal' means a mine, as in the place name Baldhu. Some names are highly picturesque like Ale and Cakes, Ding Dong or Ting Tang, or they record the wife or daughter of the mineral lord or chief adventurer, such as Wheal Emma. When a mine struck rich, neighbours would sometimes incorporate the same name, both in hope and to encourage investment. Shafts were often named after persons including the mine manager or captain. Likewise, large engines took on the name of the shaft or the engineer who designed them.

Towanroath Shaft, Wheal Coates M.J.M.

The older Cornish mines were run on the Cost Book system, which did not allow for re-investing profits in equipment for future development. A group of adventurers met periodically to receive profits, or pay a further sum to meet immediate costs. The adventurers might be a combination of mineral lords (usually the landowners), smelters or working miners.

Joseph T. Treffry is a good example of a local industrialist with the faith to invest widely in his mines, quarries, railways and harbour at Par. The mining engineer John Taylor and his sons were involved in the successful development of the Consolidated and other mines in Cornwall, in addition to mines elsewhere in Britain and abroad. They became mineral agents to the Duchy of Cornwall, and Taylor brought several new innovations into mining in the county. The mineral lords received dues on all ores sold and could do well even though a mine was not in profit. Francis Basset (created Lord de Dunstanville in 1796) was a major lord around Camborne, where he was concerned with the welfare of the miners. His monument stands on Carn Brea.

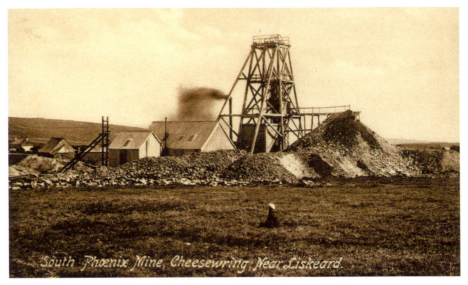

South Phoenix Mine, abortively re-opened for tin for a few years 1906 to 1911 COLLECTION M.J.M.

The 'old men' were the earliest miners to work the backs of the lodes to a shallow depth, leaving behind lines of pits and burrows on the surface, but there soon came a point when drainage was necessary. The ideal mine was on a hillside where an adit (drainage level) could be driven in from the lowest point, to follow the lode or reach it and discover new ones far under the hill. The greatest was the County Adit which was begun in 1748 from Bissoe Bridge at the head of the Carnon valley, and drained numerous mines through its 31 miles [50km] of branches. Shafts were sunk on the lode or to intersect it far below. Depths were measured in fathoms, and levels were driven from the shaft to develop the lode often at 10 fathom [18.3m] intervals. The lode might be 3-30 feet [1-9m] wide and it was worked out between two levels in a stope. The management employed mine captains who supervised the underground work. These were highly skilled miners upon whom the future success of a mine might depend. Engineers were essential to tend the engines and machinery above and below ground. There

Miners loading a wagon from an underground ore-shoot.

were two types of miner. Tributers were the skilled men who worked the mineral lode, taking a share of the value of the ore sent to the surface. 'Pitches' were auctioned on setting days at the count house, going to the lowest bidding team or 'pare' of tributers. A month's work could be highly profitable or disastrous depending on the quantity of ore broken. In addition, tools, candles and explosives had to be paid for by the men. Tutworkers made a contract to break unpayable ground at a certain sum per fathom, namely development work such as sinking shafts and driving levels.

Using a rock-drill underground.

A team of miners worked a core or shift of eight hours, and used a hand borer driven by sledge hammers for making shot holes for blasting - at first gunpowder and then more powerful explosives, tamped home with a copper-tipped rod. Premature explosions or miss-fires were common causes of accidents, although safety fuses saved many lives after 1831. Broken rock and ore was wheeled or trammed to the shaft, where it was

Dolcoath Mine in 1893. This view illustrates the extent of a major mine and its neighbours. CORNISH STUDIES LIBRARY

Michell's Shaft of East Pool and Agar Mine at the end of the nineteenth century. The engine house on the left is the now preserved whim engine and this photograph graphically illustrates the difference between a working mine and the lifeless preserved scene of today. CORNISH STUDIES LIBRARY

raised to the surface in an iron bucket or kibble until special skips were developed. Whenever possible, waste rock was backfilled in the stope, supported on timbers known as stulls.

Compressed air rock drills were seen in some tin mines after 1868, although it was not until the following decade that they were used in any numbers. For development work in driving levels they became essential because of their speed and economies in the face of foreign competition, yet some mines were reluctant to take the initial high investment. The new drills created much dust and danger to health until water was applied through a hole in the centre of the drill rod.

Ladders were the means of

Miners underground on a man-engine.

descending the early mines, and climbing these again after a hard shift took the toll of a miner's health. A German invention of great benefit was the man-engine, first employed at Tresavean mine near Redruth in 1842. Within a few years this was working down to 290 fathoms [530m], but only relatively few mines installed the machine. It was similar to a pumping beam engine, with a rod down the shaft. There were steps on the rod at the same spacing as the stroke of the beam, about 10 feet [3m], and platforms in the shaft at similar intervals allowed miners to step on and off and thus be carried up or down. Ladders continued to be used in many mines until the late 1880s when cages and gigs became more common.

Surface workers were paid on a daily basis and ore dressers included a high proportion of women and children. For example, the huge Consolidated and United mines at St Day employed 869 women and 597 children out of a total workforce of 3,196 in 1837. 'Bal maidens' were the girls who worked on a Cornish mine and conditions were tough, often in the open air with no shelters in the early years.

PUMPING

Cornish mines were notoriously wet, so pumping was necessary when below the water table or adit level. This was first overcome by rag and chain pumps operated by men, horses or waterwheels. When a waterwheel could not be built near a shaft, the power was transmitted through flat rods of timber or iron and carried on posts with dolly wheels to allow a back and forth motion. An angle bob transferred the power to a vertical motion to work the pumps in the shaft. Sometimes, pumping wheels were erected underground. By 1778, two shared the same water between the surface and adit level in Bullen Garden Mine (later part of Dolcoath) at Camborne, supplementing the work of two 'fire engines' on the same mine. Some mines employed many wheels at the surface for pumping, winding and crushing, and elaborate leats were constructed to bring them water from several miles away.

The first Newcomen 'atmospheric' steam engine in Cornwall is believed to have been erected for pumping at Wheal Vor by 1716. These early beam engines were a great advance on previous methods of pumping, but were so wasteful on fuel in a county far from the coal fields that Parliament helped the mines by granting a drawback of duty on coals brought coastwise for 'fire engines' in 1741. After a slow start, over 60 Newcomen engines had been

Unity Wood Mine between Chacewater and St Day M.J.M.

erected by the time the first Boulton and Watt engine was started at Chacewater Mine in 1777. Other engines soon followed, bringing a three-fold improvement and reduction in fuel costs, but further real development was restricted until the expiry in 1800 of their patent which was the cause of ill-feeling and frustration on both sides. In these inventive times, Boulton and Watt sent William Murdock to erect engines in Cornwall, where he invented gas lighting at his home in Redruth.

Richard Trevithick, Jonathon Hornblower and Arthur Woolf proved that there was room for improvement, and more subtle refinements were made by local engineers who knew and loved their engines well. Among Trevithick's contributions was the high pressure

The engine house at Prince of Wales' shaft of Phoenix Mine in 1907 in the course of erection with the shaft in the foreground commencing sinking. COLLECTION G. J. CHILDS

boiler and his first true Cornish beam engine was erected in 1812.

Thus the engines were available to meet the needs of the mines as they increased in depth and production in the nineteenth century. A competitive atmosphere was encouraged after 1810 by the publication of Lean's Engine Reporter, giving the 'duty' of engines, measured by the number of pounds of water which could be raised one foot high using a bushel of coal.

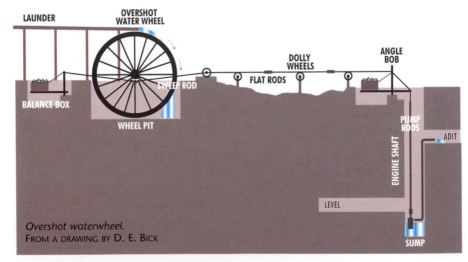

Overshot waterwheel.
FROM A DRAWING BY D. E. BICK

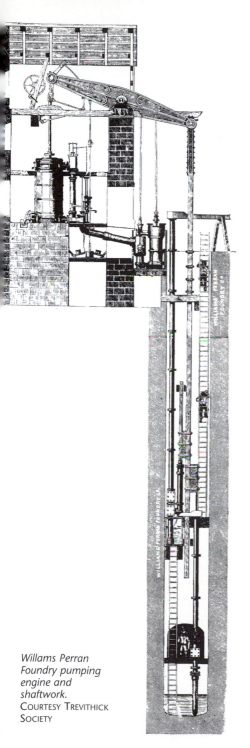

Willams Perran
Foundry pumping
engine and
shaftwork.

The cylinder size of a beam engine was measured in inches, and 80 inches diameter or more was considered to be large. Austen's 80-inch engine triumphed in a trial of 1835 at Fowey Consols, but this was pushed into third place in 1841 by the greatest of them all, Taylor's 85-inch engine at United Mines. A model of this engine can be seen in the Science Museum, South Kensington. Three-quarters of the mines on which steam engines were surveyed until this time were for copper. In 1865, there were probably over 600 engines on all mines in Cornwall. The Cornish beam engine had a long and reliable history. The last to work on a Cornish mine was stopped in 1955 at South Crofty, its work being taken over by electric pumps. The 90-inch pumping engine at nearby East Pool stopped the year before and can be visited by the public.

A pumping engine was normally erected in a house placed so that the pump rod - made of thick timber lengths bolted together - could hang down the shaft where it worked plunger pole lifts. These had replaced the less efficient bucket pumps after the 1780s. As the beam and rod descended, so water was forced up through iron pipes in stages in the shaft. To counteract the enormous weight of the pump rod, balance bobs were attached at the surface and also underground in a deep shaft. Occasionally, a pumping engine worked a shaft from a short distance away by flat rods. Tall shears were erected at the shaft to handle the heavy pitwork and pumping gear, being worked by a large capstan.

The preserved rotative whim engine at East Pool Mine, now in the care of the National Trust P.S.

WINDING

Horse whims were extensively employed for winding ores to the surface, and some pumping. They are said to have been first introduced to Cornwall by the Costers, copper smelters of Bristol, who held interests in the copper mines around St Day during the early eighteenth century. Horse whims were cheap and used on smaller mines and trial shafts down into the twentieth century. Being of timber construction and easily removed, the only evidence today might be the circular horse-round with a granite centre stone.

Watt applied his beam engine for winding in 1781. The motion was converted to a rotary one at first by his sun and planet gearing, and later a crank, with a large flywheel and winding drum. These engines were soon seen on the Cornish mines. The same rotative beam engines were also applied to stamping tin ores when the water stamps were unable to meet the demand of increased output. A 30-inch rotative whim or winding engine is preserved in its house at East Pool.

A horse whim in use at Wheal Busy at the turn of the century. The kibble in which the ores were raised can be seen behind the horse.

TIN STREAMING

This was the simplest method to get tin stone, used from prehistoric times onwards. Bodmin Moor was the stannary division of Foweymore, where the medieval tinners were probably part-time farmers. Most valleys show signs of tin-streaming, and even the marshes have been disturbed where the gravels lay beneath the peat. The, Fowey, De Lank, Penpont, St Neot and Witheybrook valleys were all worked, and deep gullies have been created over the years in the vicinity of Caradon Hill and Buttern Hill. On the east side of the St Austell district, the Red Moor was once important and has been the subject of interest in modern times. Off the granite, there were extensive and deep streamworks in the valley above Pentewan. Below St Day, the Carnon valley was worked all the way down through Bissoe to Devoran on the Restronguet Creek. Indeed, the tin deposits in the creek itself were mined via a level driven from a shaft on the shore at Point, lastly in the 1870s. In the Helston district, Porkellis Moor was streamed over the ages, and in the first half of the eighteenth century attempts were made to dredge the Loe Pool for tin with a sailing barge fitted with a wheel and

A moorland streamworks near Buttern Hill on Bodmin Moor in 1907 B.G.S.

buckets. Many of the small valleys around Penzance have been streamed for tin too.

The method of working was to remove the overburden by shovel and move it aside by wheelbarrow to gain the tin bearing gravel. This was taken out and placed on a tye, a sloping trough with water flowing over it to wash away the lighter gravels and leave behind the heavier tin stones. This material was then sorted and concentrated in a small tye, or gounce. The old working was backfilled with overburden from the next section as the excavation progressed in stages, leaving distinct patterns behind. If near a river, that water had to be kept out by embankments and artificial channels. Hand pumps or small waterwheels were also used to drain the workings. Leats were built to convey water for the wheels and the washing, processes. Small floating dredgers, such as used in Malaya, were tried unsuccessfully near Buttern Hill before 1912, and on the Goss Moor in 1925. A steam excavator was used beside the Hayle river south of St Erth in the late 1920s.

Great quantities of silt from the streamworks, mines and stamping mills were deposited by rivers in their valleys, and continuously improving techniques and separation processes have allowed these to be worked. Much of the material from the Carnon valley was deposited in the tidal Restronguet Creek where the port of Devoran faced a continual dredging problem. The Hayle and Par estuaries were also severely choked by such waste over the centuries. Flowing north from around Camborne, the whole length of the aptly named Red River was full of tin-works which gained a living by recovering the fine material brought down from the mines upstream. Various attempts have been made to dredge sea sand for its tin content off Gwithian, at the mouth of the Red River.

Once raised to the surface, the tin ore was first broken by hand (ragged and spalled) into smaller sizes in preparation for stamping, or crushing. It was only towards the end of the nineteenth century that mechanical stone-breakers took over this job. Cornish stamps had sets of four or more vertical lifters of timber or wrought iron, each with a

Bal-maidens cobbing ores.

heavy iron head in a mortar box at the base. A waterwheel turned a barrel with cams which raised and released the stampheads in rapid succession, thus crushing to a fine texture the ore which was fed in beneath. The deafening roar was heard day and night in the tin mining districts, where every stream had a succession of small stamping mills.

A rotative steam engine was first applied to stamping on Wheal Fanny (Carn Brea) in 1813. Such engines were reliable and could work more stampheads than water power. For example, in 1870 two engines at Dolcoath worked batteries of 120 and 60 stamps each; a further 20 were worked by a waterwheel in winter. Many smaller mines and streamworks continued to use water stamps. The first Californian stamps appeared in Cornwall in 1857 and became the most common type by the turn of the century. They were faster than the Cornish stamps, and their self-rotating heads allowed for even wear. Patent pneumatic stamps were built locally after 1870 by Harvey & Co. and Holman Bros., and could deal with greater quantities of ore.

After stamping, the next stage was to use gravity to separate the heavier tin. This required complex processes, so only the main ones of the nineteenth century are described here. Rectangular buddles were part of this process, but round convex buddles were introduced in about 1848. These were about 20 feet [6m] in diameter, with rotating brushes to help distribute the material as it was fed in at the centre. The lighter fines were

Water powered stamps manufactured by Williams Perran Foundry COURTESY TREVITHICK SOCIETY

Kieves, Dolcoath dressing floors in 1904 COLLECTION P.S

washed outwards, leaving behind a tin concentrate which was later dug out. Finer material was processed in concave buddles. The finest 'slimes' were concentrated on rotating round frame tables. These were of timber and were used at many valley streamworks recovering waste brought down from mines upstream.

Round buddles were costly in labour, so in the 1890s the larger tin mines such as Dolcoath installed mechanical Vanner and Wilfley tables. Both used a vibrating motion to separate out the tin concentrate as it passed over in a continuous stream. Nothing was wasted, the richer tailings being returned and run through again to extract the last particles of tin. Long rag frames were erected to catch the last 'slimes' from the plant. A final stage of concentrating tin was tossing it in a kieve, a bucket part-filled with water. The mixture was stirred before the kieve was tapped hard, making the heavier tin stuff sink rapidly.

As the mines deepened, the tin ore contained more sulphides, making it necessary to remove any impurities before smelting. Arsenopyrite was oxidised by roasting the concentrate. By 1829 the Brunton calciner had come into use, with a slowly rotating hearth upon which the concentrate was mixed as it was heated. The arsenic soot was collected in a series of chambers (a 'lambreth'). About 40 years later came the Oxland and Hocking rotating cylindrical calciner.

Having a similar specific gravity, wolfram was difficult to separate from tin. In 1844, Robert Oxland's new process converted the wolfram to tungstate of soda, which dissolved in water and found a use in the textile industry. Magnetic separation was later applied to wolfram. Modern tin dressing methods include crushing the ore in a ball mill and using froth flotation to separate the gangue minerals.

Convex buddle, King Edward Mine P.S.

26

Cornish beam engine powered stamps at Levant Mine, at the end of the nineteenth century. The noise from these would have been deafening. ROYAL INSTITUTION OF CORNWALL

COPPER ORE DRESSING

The dressing of copper ores was less complex than that for tin, but employed much more labour. Being weaker, copper ores were first sorted and spalled (broken) by hand at the surface, where many women and children were employed. The 'bal maidens' handled special pointed hammers to reduce the better ores to a chestnut size, an operation called cobbing. At the bucking mills, they used flat hammers to reduced the ore further to the size of a pea or bean.

Powered crushing rollers replaced bucking and became more common after the 1830s, although the ores were still picked and cobbed by hand. Poorer ores were crushed in stamps. The finer ores were treated by jigging, whereby a sieve was agitated up and down in a box part-filled with water. The ore in suspension was concentrated by removing the lighter material at the top. Along with the crushing rollers, the jig was mechanised and first introduced by John Taylor at the Consolidated Mines in 1831. Once prepared for sale, the copper ore was piled in 'parcels' at the mine or the shipping quays where they were assayed and bid for by the smelters' agents.

With the growth of so many mines in Cornwall came the establishment of related industries. Harvey & Co.'s foundry at Hayle made mining equipment and sent Cornish beam engines to mines at home and abroad, to Australia, South Africa and the Americas, as well as waterworks and drainage schemes. Others making beam engines were the Copperhouse Foundry at Hayle, Williams' Perran Foundry at Perranarworthal, and

The Mining Exchange, at Redruth P.S.

William West's St Blazey foundry. Holman Bros. of Camborne manufactured mining machinery and drilling equipment, and although all the mines around have closed, the firm still makes equipment under the name of CompAir Holman Ltd. The same is true for the famous Camborne School of Mines which maintains a high standard and takes in students from all over the world. Born out of earlier schools in 1888, it moved to modern premises at Pool in 1975, within sight of South Crofty Mine.

Carvedras Smelting Works, at Truro, about 1912. Behind is the timber Carvedras Viaduct of the Cornwall Railway. ROYAL INSTITUTION OF CORNWALL

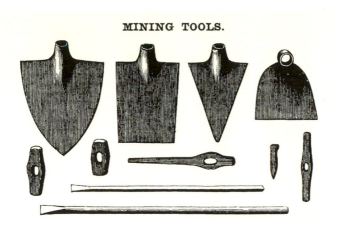

MINING TOOLS.

Explosives for mines were manufactured in Cornwall, with notable gunpowder mills at Kennal Vale and Herodsfoot. High explosives were introduced and manufactured in the second half of the nineteenth century at Hayle and Perranporth. Nitroglycerine and guncotton were tried in the mines in the 1860s, and dynamite was in use by 1871. In 1831, William Bickford invented the safety fuse, which was made in a factory at Tuckingmill near Camborne for exactly 130 years.

THE MINING POPULATION

Mining had a far greater effect on the rise and fall of population than any other industry in Cornwall. In the nineteenth century the greatest increases were in the Camborne-Redruth and St Day districts. Gwennap, which contained the richest copper ore body, was the most populous parish in Cornwall in 1841.

The movement of miners to new districts brought a Klondyke atmosphere to the new mining villages such as Pensilva near Liskeard. There were overcrowded lodgings before enough cottages could be built, and heavy drinking and riots were not uncommon among some of the miners on pay day. In contrast, Methodism was strong in many communities where the working populace had been strongly influenced by John Wesley in the latter part of the eighteenth century. One of his favourite preaching places was Gwennap Pit, apparently formed by collapsed mine workings near St Day and since terraced by his followers. He last preached there in August 1789 at the age of 86 to many thousands of miners. In the following century, Billy Bray was a well known miner and preacher from Baldhu.

In the copper slump of the 1860s it was the mining parishes which were hardest hit by mass emigration. In the 18 months ending December 1867, over 11,000 had lost their jobs in the mining districts of Cornwall and west Devon. Some found work in the china clay industry, or other mining districts in Britain, but many were proud of their skills and emigrated to North and South America, South Africa or Australia. These 'Cousin Jacks' sent money to their families who remained at home. Others took their families with them, so that there are now Cornish communities in most of the metal mining centres of the world. There is much truth in the saying that wherever there is a mine there is a Cornishman at the bottom of it!

Cornish bal-maidens.

Emigration was not new, for already a few Cornishmen had been taking their expertise to other mines in Britain and abroad. These included the inventor Richard Trevithick who in 1816 went out to supervise the installation of his high pressure engines in Peruvian silver mines, and spent the next 11 years in South America. In the early 1850s, the deeper mines around St Just were already short of skilled miners who had left for the goldfields of Australia and America.

The mining industry brought prosperity to the larger towns and many buildings reflect this today. Once thriving mining villages retain terraces of simple cottages, and it is easy to forget the desolation brought about by the closure of the mines. As an example, St Day parish was hard hit when six mines were abandoned in 1871-8, causing the loss of 3,450 jobs. The population decreased by 20%, and 12% of the houses were reported unoccupied and many others dilapidated.

THE EVIDENCE TODAY

Roofless engine houses dominate the surface remains of a disused mine today, and have survived because they had to be built solidly. Being the thickest, the bob wall on which the beam rested is often the last to fall when the building becomes ruinous. The opposite wall has a broad arch through which the cylinder was installed. Rarely, this arch was built at the side of the house, as at West Chiverton. The architectural style varied according to the builder, the materials available locally, or how much the mine could afford. Window openings may have brick, stone or timber lintels. Inside the engine house may be seen the granite bed stones for the cylinder, with mighty bolt holes.

The boiler houses alongside were built less sturdily, as they only had to support a roof over perhaps four long Cornish or Lancashire boilers. They were often demolished when the boilers were removed, so they are easily forgotten. Traces can be found, but there are a few good examples left.

Chimney stacks are characteristically Cornish - round in section, stone-built but finished off at the top in brick. Very few examples are otherwise. They may stand alone, at the end of the boiler house, or built into the corner of the engine house.

On a deserted mine, the largest house is usually for the pumping engine, which did the heaviest work. It is sited next to the shaft collar, where the balance bob pit and capstan round can sometimes be seen. The empty whim or winding engine house is set back from the shaft and often at right angles to the pumping engine house. The clue is the stone platform ('loading') which supported the winding drum and flywheel beneath the bob wall. The stamps engine house will be elsewhere, again with evidence of the flywheel position and the foundations for the stamps battery in front. Often overlooked is the now dried up engine pool which supplied water for the boilers and for condensing.

The layout of a mine often seems a haphazard affair, developed piecemeal on any available space as it became more productive. Apart from the engine houses, the count house or mine office might survive as a dwelling. The bigger mines had drying houses where the underground men changed, while elsewhere they may have used the boiler house of an engine. Compressor houses are later additions to the layout. On the site of the dressing floors, one would expect round buddles to be notable features.

Wherever possible, waterwheels were used for pumping, winding, stamping or working dressing plant, and wheelpits can be found on a number of mine sites. Some are large and their now dry leats can still be followed for a considerable distance. Evidence at the surface does not always tell the true tale, for some rich mines have been so destroyed that there is little to see at the surface, while other mines which made no profit have left the most interesting remains.

Crowns Shaft, Botallack Mine P.S.

This gazetteer describes a personal choice of sites to visit. The mines have been grouped in districts based on the best centre from which to explore them. Using the grid references, the Ordnance Survey 1:50,000 Landranger map is adequate to find the sites, but the larger scale 1:25,000 Explorer map is recommended for a more detailed investigation. Inclusion should not imply automatic right of access - if in doubt, seek permission from the landowner. Always beware of unfenced shafts and unstable masonry, and remember, underground exploration can be dangerous! In addition, Cornwall's mine waste dumps or burrows contain a great variety of minerals of interest to the geologist.

PENZANCE DISTRICT

Here lived the tinners described long ago by Diodorus Siculus, probably including the inhabitants of the ancient Chysauster village [SW 4733501], and tin continued to be streamed in the valleys of this West Penwith peninsula for centuries. The remains of an old wooden waterwheel and rag and chain pump were found buried at Drift Moor near Penzance when the tin workings were reopened in about 1813.

Most nineteenth-century tin and copper mining was along the north coast, especially around St Just and Pendeen. Some mines extended beneath the sea, and on stormy days it was alarming to hear boulders being rolled about on the sea bed above. Eastwards are the remains of small mines, such as at Gurnard's Head and around Zennor. St Ives was the centre of more activity, with some mines at the town's edge and around Carbis Bay. In the south, there was the unusual Wherry Mine, sunk just offshore between Penzance and Newlyn, but destroyed when a drifting ship collided with it in 1798.

The St Just mines were never served by a mineral railway, and all ores and coals were taken by road to and from Penzance as the rugged north coast was unsuitable for shipping. Mining maintained Penzance as a port, where there was a considerable trade in supplies of coal and timber. Copper ore and tin blocks were exported, for tin was smelted at nearby Chyandour from before 1758 until 1912. St Ives was the scene of experimental shipments of copper ore from St Just in the late sixteenth century, but later shipments were small and intermittent. Hayle came under the Customs port of St Ives until 1864, but this major port mostly served the mines to the east. The harbour at St Michael's Mount came under Penzance, but shipped ores from the Helston district. The Geevor Tin Mine Museum at Pendeen is well worth visiting, while the Wayside Folk Museum at Zennor includes some mining exhibits. In Penzance, the Museum of the Royal Geological Society of Cornwall has an important collection of minerals.

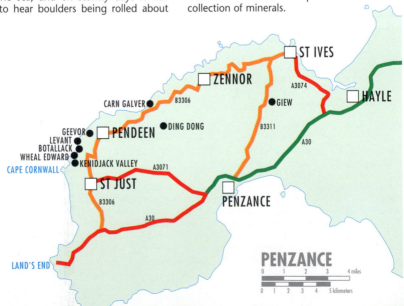

BOTALLACK MINE
[SW 362336]

Famous for the two engine houses crouched on a small ledge close to the sea on the Crowns section of the mine, restored by the Carn Brea Mining Society in 1985. The lower house had a 30-inch pumping engine in about 1835, and the chimney stack was placed inside the building to save space. The other engine house of 1862 had an enclosed winder for the Diagonal Shaft, sunk to 1,360 feet [414m] below sea level and descended in 1865 by the Duke and Duchess of Cornwall (later King Edward VII and Queen Alexandra). Victoria and Albert had visited Botallack in 1846, and Wilkie Collins wrote a terrifying account of his descent in 1850. The opening to the shaft can be seen cut from the rocky cliff just above the waves.

There was an extensive mine layout above the cliffs, with 11 steam engines in 1865 when 500 persons were employed. Most of the mine ceased in March 1895 due to low tin prices, but some work continued in the shallow levels. Botallack was reworked in 1907-14, when dressing floors and arsenic flues (a 'lambreth') were built on the cliff top. Most recently, a steel headframe was erected over Allen's Shaft during explorations in the early 1980s. The nearby count house has been restored.

CAPE CORNWALL MINE
[SW 350318]

An ornamental brick stack is a landmark on the summit of the pyramidal cape. It was for a whim engine lower down on the south side, but created such a draught that it was soon replaced. The old boiler house and the count house are now dwellings. Cape Cornwall Mine was the most westerly in England and last worked for tin in about 1873. The ruins of St Just United, another mine which worked beneath the sea, are above Priest's Cove to the south east.

CARN GALVER MINE
[SW 421364]

Two ruined engine houses next to the B3306 coast road have been partly restored by the National Trust. They were built for a 40-inch pumping engine (west) and a 20-inch whim engine (east). Unusually, the latter faces away from the shaft. The mine was part of Morvah & Zennor United Mine, but produced little tin when last worked in the 1870s. The main shaft is 130 fathoms [238m] deep. The count house is now a climbing hut for climbers visiting the impressive Bosigran cliffs. Down near the cliffs, before the stream cascades into Porthmoina

Carn Galver Mine P.S.

Cove, are the ruins of a tin mill with a wheelpit [SW 418367]. A deep adit can be seen emerging at the back of the cove.

DING DONG MINE
[SW 435344]

Ding Dong is said to have been worked for tin back in Roman times, but the ruins belong to the period 1814-78 when the mine reached a depth of 135 fathoms [247m]. The pumping engine house at Greenburrow Shaft is a most conspicuous landmark high up on the inland moors of West Penwith. It was built in 1865 for a 30-inch engine, and has been the subject of restoration work. Old shafts extend north east towards two other engine houses, the best for a whim at SW 441348. The mine is not far from the prehistoric Lanyon Quoit, Men-an-Tol and Nine Maidens stone circle, making this a varied and interesting place to visit.

Victory Shaft, Geevor Mine P.S.

GEEVOR TIN MINE
[SW 375345]
The last tin mine in the district was worked by Geevor Tin Mines Ltd from 1911 until 1986, when the tin market crash caused nearly 300 men to be laid off. Distress among the mining communities of Pendeen and St Just was reminiscent of a century before. The mine was left on a care and maintenance basis, with the pumps kept going, in the hope of a recovery of tin prices, but was closed in 1990. Towards the sea is the steel headframe above the main Victory Shaft, named appropriately in 1919, and below this are the tin dressing mills. The smaller Treweeks Shaft was opened in 1967. Geevor is connected to Levant Mine and much development work, with an inclined underground shaft, took place before operations were halted. Beside the B3306 at Pendeen is the old timber headframe of Wethered Shaft [SW 378341]. Since it closed as a working tin mine, the site has become the Geevor Tin Mine Museum. There are mining exhibits in the old buildings and guided tours around the twentieth-century surface workings and underground in part of an eighteenth-century mine.

GIEW MINE
[SW 501369]
A mine in a commanding position on the flanks of Trink Hill beside the B3311 at Cripple's Ease, where the pub is the Engine Inn. The house for a 50-inch pumping engine at Frank's Shaft (217 fathoms deep) is given an unusual appearance by its truncated chimney stack. Concrete foundations of an electric power station and winder date from the last working for tin by the St Ives Consolidated Mines Ltd. in 1907. Giew continued alone in 1915-22, and was the only active tin producer in Cornwall in its last two years. There are further remains in the vicinity, including foundations of the dressing mill and a small powder magazine.

KENIDJACK VALLEY
[SW 370319 to 356322]
The narrow Kenidjack or Nancherrow valley meets the sea just north east of Cape Cornwall, and its floor is rich in industrial remains. There were tin stamping mills and dressing floors, but foremost is the ruined arsenic works [SW 360323], with remains of flues and a stack. At the lower end near the sea is a large masonry wheelpit [SW 356322] for a 52 foot [15.8m] wheel which pumped via flat rods in the 1860s. Thirty years before, the valley boasted a wheel of 65 feet [19.8m], the largest in Cornwall. There are traces of watercourses everywhere.

LEVANT MINE
[SW 368345]
Levant was a dry mine despite running out over a mile [1.6 km] beneath the sea, working to 350 fathoms [640m] below adit. Its main history began as a copper mine in about 1820, but tin was produced after 1852. Copper continued to be mined until 1910 making this Cornwall's last copper mine.

In 1919 came a terrible disaster, when the man-engine collapsed killing 31 miners and injuring many others. Thereafter Levant struggled on until 1930. The sea breached the mine but the hole was plugged in the 1960s and development work took place from the adjacent Geevor Mine.

A 24-inch whim engine built in 1840 by Harveys of Hayle is preserved inside a tiny engine house on the edge of a cliff at Skip Shaft and is owned by the National Trust. It was saved in 1935 by the Cornish Engines Preservation Society and has since been restored to steam working by volunteer members of the Trevithick Society. The empty house here had a 45-inch pumping engine. Up behind, a tall chimney with a coursed brickwork top stands above the old compressor house built in 1901 for underground rock drills and winding. A low stack was for the horizontal man-engine, of which there are traces of the shaft and access steps. There are also the remains of two circular powder magazines.

WHEAL EDWARD

[SW 362328]

Two weather-beaten engine houses stand on the cliff to the south of Botallack Mine. There were two inclined shafts beneath the sea, one starting near the western engine house. Tin and copper were produced, and other minerals included uranium and pitchblende. The mine has not worked since 1893, when 19 men and a boy were drowned when the old flooded workings of neighbouring Wheal Owles were holed.

HELSTON DISTRICT

Helston was one of the ancient coinage towns, at the centre of a large district with tin and copper mines in a belt north east from Marazion. Tin was important around Wendron, where Porkellis Moor was streamed for years. The district had a celebrated tin mine at Wheal Vor, just east of Tregonning Hill. First recorded in the fifteenth century, it is said that gunpowder was first used here, as was the first steam pumping engine in Cornwall. During the nineteenth century it was a fabulously rich tin mine and even had its own smelting works. It reached a depth of 295 fathoms [539m], pumped dry by seven engines. Yet the mine has left little to see today. Two miles [3.2 km] to the north, Crenver and Wheal Abraham was at one time the most important and deepest copper mine in Cornwall, but again there is nothing significant left except burrows, illustrating the fact that the quality of the surface remains is not always an indicator of a mine's former glory.

Some copper ores from the parishes of Marazion and St Hilary were shipped at St Michael's Mount, the Ictis of the ancient tin

Great Work Mine P.S.

traders. Gweek, at the head of the Helford River, was the old port for Helston and shipped quantities of tin from the district. Porthleven harbour was built in 1811-25 with the hope of encouraging trade from the Wendron mines and others to the south of Hayle.

BASSET & GRYLLS MINE

[SW 693329]

Formerly known as Porkellis Mine, this tin mine was worked in the latter half of the nineteenth century and tried three times in the twentieth century. A small restored engine house is beside a lane just south of Porkellis village.

GREAT WORK MINE

[SW 596307]

This rich tin mine was at work in the sixteenth century, when about 300 miners were employed. It was worked in 1816-73 for tin, employing 500 people and five engines. A pumping engine house at Leeds' Shaft is a reminder of those days and is a landmark on the saddle between Tregonning and Godolphin Hills. It has an unusual chimney stack with its upper brickwork in two stages. The mine was unwatered in an attempt to rework it in the 1930s.

Tregurtha Downs Mine, near Marazion. The 80 inch pumping engine is now at South Crofty Mine and this engine house has been converted to a private house COLLECTION P.S.

POLDARK MINE
[SW 683315]
Part of the underground workings of the old Wendron Consols is now a tourist attraction at Wendron, while outside are displays of machinery. These include a rotative beam engine of about 1850, which worked in the St Austell district, first at the Bunny tin mine before pumping clay slurry at Greensplatt china clay pit from 1894 until 1959. It was the last to work in Cornwall and was moved to Wendron in the winter of 1972/3. A museum tells of early tin working and the Cornish miner overseas.

PORKELLIS MOOR STREAMWORKS
[SW 688325]
Porkellis Moor is in the upper part of the Cober valley and has been disturbed by centuries of alluvial tin workings. The valley bottom to the south and west of Porkellis is overgrown and pitted with pools. The Poldark Mine is just downstream.

TREGURTHA DOWNS MINE
[SW 538310]
The mine was worked for copper and then tin several times, the last main attempt in 1882-95, but small ventures continued into the twentieth century. It lies just north west of Goldsithney and is dominated by an impressive pumping engine house with a slate roof and a fine chimney. Tall narrow windows like arrow slits make it similar to the house at East Wheal Rose (St Agnes district), but this one has been re-roofed and made habitable. A famous pumping engine was installed here with a new 80-inch cylinder in 1883. It had been built at Hayle in 1854 and already served on two mines. After

stopping, it was removed to South Crofty (Camborne district) in 1903 where it worked until 1955 and is still preserved.

WHEAL PROSPER
[SW 594270]
The National Trust has restored a 30-inch pumping engine house which stands on a shelf on the steep slope above Rinsey Cove. Despite its name, the mine worked briefly in 1860-6, producing only a little copper and tin.

WHEAL TREWAVAS
[SW 599265]
This copper mine on the east side of the granite Trewavas Head was worked under the sea until it was flooded and closed. In 1836-46, about 17,500 tons of ore were produced and probably shipped from just along the coast at Porthleven. Two engines were installed in the 1830s and their houses are perched down the cliffs, their seaward walls being taller to compensate for the slope. The western engine house has a capstan round built on a stone platform. Trewavas Head is best reached along the cliff path from Wheal Prosper at Rinsey Cove.

CAMBORNE & REDRUTH DISTRICT

This was by far the greatest centre of the Cornish mining industry. There is now surprisingly little evidence of mining activity along the foot of Carn Brea between Camborne and Redruth, where old photographs show scores of smoking chimney stacks. To the south, however, a long run of engine houses following the Great Flat Lode can be explored by a signposted trail.
The mines were well served with mineral railways to the ports of Devoran, Hayle and Portreath. To the north was Portreath, which still exists with a pier and two small docks [SW 656454]. The Portreath Tram Road was a plateway built in 1812 by the Williams family from Poldice mine in the St Day district. After 1826, the Redruth & Chasewater Railway to Devoran [SW 795390] served the mines of St Day and the south side of Redruth, where a branch to Wheal Buller crossed one from the Hayle Railway to Tresavean mine. The latter railway dates from 1837, becoming the West Cornwall Railway nine years later. There was a branch from the Camborne mines which descended an impressive incline to Portreath, while the main line went to the quays at Hayle. Here the Copperhouse Dock [SW568380] was constructed of slag blocks when smelting took place here. This once important mining port has sadly declined and

just a fraction of the great Harvey's foundry at Carnsew has been preserved.

Arsenic was calcined at several sites. One magnificent pair of chimney stacks stood at Tolvaddon between Camborne and Redruth, before they were demolished in 1975 during the construction of the A30 by-pass. A lone stack, formerly taller, can be seen near the A30 west of Camborne at SW 606401. This was for the Roseworthy arsenic works, sited in the valley below.

The towns of Camborne and Redruth have terraces of miners' houses and some notable buildings. The latter has William Murdock's house and the Mining Exchange of 1863 in Alma Place near the railway station. Outside Camborne's public library is a statue of Richard Trevithick (1771-1833), while the cottage in which he spent his early years is maintained by the National Trust in the nearby hamlet of Penponds [SW 637389]. At Pool, the Camborne School of Mines has a geological museum which contains mineral specimens from local mines.

BASSET MINES
[SW 681394]

The Basset Mines group worked for tin in 1896-1918. Formed from the older South Frances, Wheal Basset and West Wheal Basset, they worked the Great Flat Lode to the south of Carn Brea.

There are very impressive mine buildings on the South Frances section at Marriott's Shaft [SW 681394], where a compound pumping engine was set to work in 1899, with 40-inch high pressure and 80-inch low pressure cylinders. A large compressor house and other buildings are also here. Just to the west are the pumping and winding engine houses at Pascoe's Shaft [SW

Marriott's Shaft, Basset Mines, with, from left, the ore hoppers, compressor house and pumping engine house P.S.

678393]. North, beside the road at SW 681397 is a date stone 'AD 1854' in the surviving granite ashlar bob wall of a 60-inch pumping engine house on Thomas's Shaft of West Wheal Basset. Ores were sent on tramways to the stamps and dressing floors on both sides of Carnkie village. Extensive ruins include pumping, winding and stamps engine houses at SW 688402 and an unusual double stamps engine house and ore dressing (Vanner) house [SW 691399]. The old Basset count house is now a restaurant here. Nearby are the old Seleggan tin smelting works [SW 695401] and engine houses of Wheal Uny [SW 695408].

CARN BREA MINES
[SW 676409]

Nineteenth-century operations began in 1831 when this great mine worked for copper along the north foot of Carn Brea. Fifty years later tin production had become more important, the

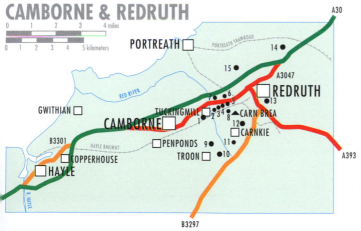

CAMBORNE & REDRUTH

1 DOLCOATH
2 COOK'S KITCHEN
3 TINCROFT
4 SOUTH CROFTY
5&6 EAST POOL ENGINES
    & DISCOVERY CENTRE
7 CAMBORNE SCHOOL OF MINES
8 CARN BREA
9 GREAT CONDURROW &
    KING EDWARD MINE
10 GRENVILLE UNITED
11 SOUTH FRANCES
12 BASSET MINES
13 PEDNANDREA
14 WHEAL PEEVOR
15 TOLGUS TIN

Cook's Kitchen Mine P.S.

mine having reached 285 fathoms [521m] with 29 miles [46.4km] of levels. It was amalgamated with Cook's Kitchen and Tincroft in 1896, the whole closing in 1921. Over 1,000 were employed on the mine which had at least 11 engines, of which survive a ruined stamps engine house and a broad-based stack in six stages.

COOK'S KITCHEN MINE
[SW 6654061]
Having worked the same lode as Dolcoath in the eighteenth century, the mine was restarted in 1832. In 1865 there were four steam engines and seven waterwheels here, one working a man-engine. Cook's Kitchen had reached a depth of 420 fathoms [768m] in 1895 when it was taken over by Tincroft Mine. Two surviving engine houses once contained 50-inch pumping and 26-inch winding engines.

DOLCOATH MINE
[SW 661403]
This renowned Cornish mine started its life for copper in the 1720s, although competition from Anglesey caused its closure for a few years in the 1790s. It was a rich copper mine, reaching 240 fathoms [439m] by 1824. As the copper began to fail, Dolcoath turned to deep tin, becoming the county's leading producer until the Great War. In 1864 there were ten engines, seven waterwheels and one man-engine at work, and 1,266 persons were employed. As a cost book mine, Dolcoath sold ores worth nearly £6,000,000 in 1799-1895. Despite a battle against falling tin prices, the mine was abandoned in 1921, having reached 550 fathoms [1,006m], the greatest depth of any Cornish mine. Today, the site is surrounded by dereliction east of Camborne, where terraced houses in Dolcoath Road were built for the miners. The few remains include a distinct roofed building with arched windows and its stack, which contained a large vertical compressor. Across the road, some buildings

later became premises for Cornwall Technical College. On the hillside to the south are the ruins of a house for a unique Holman traversing winding engine, installed here at the new Williams' Shaft in 1900 [SW 661399].

EAST POOL ENGINES & INDUSTRIAL DISCOVERY CENTRE
[SW 674415 & SW 674419]
The old copper mine of East Pool lay on the south side of the main road through Pool. It later turned to tin, and Wheal Agar to the north was taken over in 1896, the whole becoming the East Pool & Agar Mine. After the decline of Dolcoath it became the leading tin producer, with additional revenue from arsenic and wolfram. Two fine beam engines are preserved in their houses by the National Trust. A 30-inch whim engine, built by Holman Bros. in 1887, worked Michell's.Shaft until 1920. It stands immediately south of the road at Pool [SW 674415]. The second is the 90-inch pumping engine at Taylor's Shaft [SW 674419], sunk in 1922 after the old pumping shaft had collapsed. The engine was installed in 1924, having been built by Harveys of Hayle in 1892 first for Carn Brea Mine. The beam weighs 52 tons and the total weight of the engine is 125 tons. Although East Pool closed in 1945, the engine was kept going until 1954 to prevent the flooding of South Crofty. Electric pumps then took over. The easily recognised 110-foot [33.5m] stack has the initials 'EPAL' in white brick, for East Pool & Agar Ltd. and the trade name of their arsenic. Connected to this site, the Trevithick Trust has opened Cornwall's Industrial Discovery Centre in the boiler house to provide an introduction to the county's industrial and social history.

GREAT CONDURROW MINE
[SW 661393]
The well preserved pumping engine house at Neame's Shaft is a landmark near Beacon and dates from a 1907-13 reworking which only

Taylor's Shaft, East Pool & Agar Mine P.S.

produced a little tin. The engine was an 80-inch, bought second hand, having worked previously on West Chiverton and Gwennap United Mines. The shaft is 280 fathoms [512m] deep.

GRENVILLE UNITED MINES
[SW 668389]
Pumping and winding engine houses stand at Fortescue's Shaft on the Great Flat Lode. The former was for a 90-inch pumping engine, from 1892 before being moved to South Crofty. A good stamps engine house (1891) is at SW 666386, flanked on both sides by the concrete foundations for the stamps batteries.

KING EDWARD MINE
[SW 664389]
Part of the old South Condurrow Mine became the Camborne School of Mines' King Edward Mine in about 1904 and the plant was used for training students. A museum here contains original equipment and rescued plant, including Californian stamps, a buddle, round frame, shaking table and reconstructed rag frame, which demonstrate in a clear manner how ore was processed. One of the original wooden buildings contains a display of artefacts. Awaiting display is a twin cylinder hoisting engine built by Holman Bros. in 1905. The museum is alongside the Great Flat Lode Trail.

PEDNANDREA MINE
[SW 703420]
This was a rich tin mine, right within Redruth town and close to the terminus of the Redruth & Chasewater Railway. Its workings extend beneath the town to a depth of 186 fathoms [340m]. It closed in 1891, and is remembered by the lower part of a staged chimney stack which is a prominent landmark. This is said to have been 140 feet [47m] high and was for a 70-inch pumping engine.

SOUTH CROFTY MINE
[SW 664408]
South Crofty was the last working tin mine in Cornwall and can be seen from various points between Tuckingmill and Pool. South Crofty worked from 1854 until 1896, when it closed for four years because of low tin prices. In 1906 South Crofty Ltd. was formed and the mine continued thereafter, growing to take in other mines covering about 6 square miles and reaching a depth of 380 fathoms [695m]. When Robinson's Shaft was new in 1903, the 80-inch engine from Tregurtha Downs (Helston district) was erected here, and it worked until 1 May 1955, its 101st year - the last beam pumping engine to work on a tin mine in Cornwall. Although it is in the care of the National Trust,

Tolgus Tin Works P.S.

there is no public access. New Cook's Shaft was sunk in 1907, and a 90-inch engine (from Grenville Mines) erected in a concrete house worked from 1922 until 1950 when one side of the beam broke. In 1970 a new tall headframe and fast winding engine were installed here. This landmark, alongside dressing plant and ore silos, overlooks the valley above the mining village of Tuckingmill.

TINCROFT MINE
[SW 669407]
An unusual engine house stands near the railway bridge behind Carn Brea industrial estate. It was for a horizontal tandem-compound single stage air compressor, built by Harvey & Co. in about 1890, to power rock drills in the mine which became part of the Carn Brea group in 1896 until closure in 1921. Just west is an engine house with tall arched windows and a truncated chimney. Its 26-inch engine worked a man-engine from 1863. It is the only man-engine house standing in Cornwall.

TOLGUS TIN
[SW 690443]
The last of many small tin streamworks along this valley, beside the Cornish Gold attraction near Redruth. Waterwheels work Cornish stamps and a dipper wheel, and other original equipment has been restored by the Trevithick Trust to demonstrate tin processing to the public.

WHEAL PEEVOR
[SW 7084421]
This is a good survival, with three different engine houses easily visible from the A30 near Redruth. The largest, in the centre of the group, is the pumping engine house. The whim engine house is to the east, while the third engine was for driving a battery of stamps, the foundations of which are still in place. Tin was mainly produced here in 1872-89, but some work continued until 1918.

The mining village of St Day makes a good centre for exploring the district, where the copper mines of Gwennap were the richest in Cornwall. The village of miners' cottages has a ruined church containing displays on local history. Evidence of mining is all around, to the north, east and south east, where acres of devastated land have been only partly restored. The County Adit was first driven in 1784 by Sir William Lemon to drain Poldice Mine from the Carnon valley. Eventually, many more mines were drained by the adit, which with its branches extends 31 miles [50 km]. Ochre was collected from the sediment flowing from its mouth, which helped pay for its upkeep. The Carnon valley has been extensively streamed for tin and its industries included the Bissoe Arsenic Works [SW 771414]. The late twentieth century Wheal Jane and Mount Wellington tin mine sites overlook this part of the valley.

The Portreath Tram Road of 1812 had a terminus near Poldice Mine, but most ores were carried to the south. The 4-foot gauge Redruth & Chasewater Railway (1826-1915) passed through the district and had sidings onto Consolidated, United and Poldice mines. Much of its course can be followed down the Carnon valley to the interesting port of Devoran [SW 795389], now much silted up, on the Restronguet Creek. A branch line continued to a quay at Point [SW 810385], where there were tin and lead smelting works. The railway displaced the packhorses

The former clock tower at Consolidated Mines. Note the octagonal base P.S.

which formerly served shipping places on other branches of the Fal, such as Roundwood Quay [SW 838404] and Pill Quay [SW 828384].

The famous Perran Foundry was near Devoran at Perran Wharf [SW 776385], while further up the same valley the Kennall Vale gunpowder works [SW 747373] was well sited to supply the mines. Towards Truro the bell and clock tower remains of the Calenick tin smelting works [SW 821431], which worked in 1711-1891. The Royal Cornwall Museum in Truro has a fine mineral collection and exhibits relating to tin mining and smelting.

CONSOLIDATED MINES
[SW 745420]

The Consolidated Mines were established in 1819 by John Taylor, the successful mining

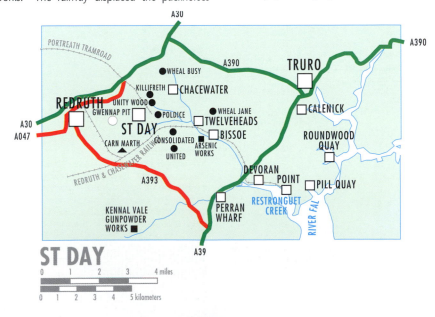

Wheal Busy, near Chacewater, with the engine and boiler house M.J.M.

engineer, and exploited the richest copper lode in the world over the next 21 years. Over 2,000 persons were employed and within seven years of its opening, Taylor had built the Redruth & Chasewater Railway to serve this and other mines. Taylor's lease was not renewed in 1840, so he took out all easily recoverable ores, leaving little for his successors. As a result, a record 23,194 tons of ore were produced in 1839. The mine was taken over in 1857 by the neighbouring United Mines, working as Clifford Amalgamated until 1870. Surprisingly little remains of this great mine today, and acres of burrows and derelict land have been recently 'restored'. Of interest is a broad stack which was for a clock tower [SW 745420]. Just below are the ruins of an engine house and stack, among the oldest in Cornwall, erected for Taylor's famous 85-inch pumping engine.

GREAT WHEAL BUSY
[SW 739448]
Once known as Chacewater Mine, this was worked periodically from about 1700 until 1920. A large Newcomen engine was erected here by the engineer John Smeaton in 1775, and two years later the first Watt engine in Cornwall was added. The remains today are more recent. A fine engine house of about 1856 had an 85-inch pumping engine installed in 1909-10. Last worked in 1924, it was not scrapped until 1945. The separate chimney stack has a notable style, and the boiler house (for three boilers) is intact with a roof. The mine carpenters' and smiths' workshops are nearby, with two cast iron lintels inscribed 'GREAT WHEAL (1872) BUSY MINES'. Just south at SW 739445 is a Brunton arsenic calciner, with condensing chambers and chimney stack, dating from 1907 when the mine was worked for arsenic.

KILLIFRETH MINE
[SW 734442]
The restored engine house at Killifreth is clearly recognisable by its extraordinary tall and slender stack, and is one of a line of engine houses and stacks seen from the road to the west of Chacewater. The stack was heightened to improve the draught for the boilers of a winder and a large 85-inch pumping engine which shared it during a reopening in 1913. Despite several attempts, Killifreth was never very successful as a tin mine.

POLDICE MINE
[SW 741429]
This was an early tin mine, which became rich in copper ore in the eighteenth and nineteenth centuries. There was a tramway to Portreath and, later, the Redruth & Chasewater Railway gave access to the much closer port of Devoran. Remains on the dressing floors include arsenic condensing chambers but date from a later re-working of the surface tips.

UNITED MINES
[SW 749416]
The workings of this other great copper mine lay south of Consolidated and included the old eighteenth-century mines of Ale & Cakes and Wheal Cupboard. John Taylor was again involved here, especially after he left Consolidated. The

Killifreth Mine M.J.M.

Mount Wellington Mine in 1977 P.S.

underground workings were hot, and temperatures of 110 degrees Fahrenheit or more were recorded in the levels which went down to 285 fathoms [521m]. United took over Consolidated in 1857, and when Wheal Clifford was included in 1861, they were named Clifford Amalgamated Mines. Alas, nine years later they were closed because of the low prices offered for copper ores. Underground workings extended over 80 miles [128 km], and at the surface were at least 18 steam engines, making the greatest collection on any mine in the world.

Little now remains, and the best preserved engine house [SW 749416] was built for a 34-inch engine working 120 stampheads when the burrows and shallow levels were re-worked for tin as Gwennap United in 1900-5. The ruined engine house at Garland's Shaft [SW 751416] was built at the same time for the 80-inch pumping engine brought from West Chiverton Mine. The small Eldon's 30-inch pumping engine house (1827-70) has been preserved beside the road at SW 747414. Much of the landscape has been 'restored' by the local authority, and a portion transformed into an industrial estate.

UNITY WOOD MINE
[SW 736436]
A pair of engine houses for pumping and winding stand beside the lane from Wheal Busy to Todpool, a mile [1.6 km] north east of St Day. The arrangement is unusual in that the winder is not at right angles to its companion. In 1851, the mine was worked for tin with its neighbours under the name of St Day United.

WHEAL JANE
[SW 771427]
In 1971, Wheal Jane was the first large Cornish tin mine to be opened for 50 years. Mining is a risky business, and it was forced to close in 1978-80 and again finally in 1991. Wheal Jane employed modern methods to produce tin and considerable quantities of copper and zinc. A huge tailings dam prevented pollution of the Carnon valley which had already suffered from centuries of activity. Another new mine, at Mount Wellington [SW 760418], was amalgamated with Wheal Jane.

ST AGNES DISTRICT

Tin was the main source of wealth at St Agnes, and some open workings along the backs of lodes around St Agnes Beacon may be medieval. This old mining district also had copper, iron and rich lead mines. West Wheal Kitty and its neighbours lie beneath St Agnes village, while along the coast few holidaymakers may realise that Perranporth is also undermined. The Great Perran Iron Lode was worked over a considerable length from the cliffs at the north end of Perran Beach. Inland, were rich lead mines which also produced silver.

The mines around St Agnes were served by the tiny Trevaunance harbour, built close under the cliff on the west side of Trevaunance Cove below the village [SW 721517]. Coal and other imports were raised by a horse and overhanging staging, while ores were let down a chute to the pier. The ore awaiting shipment was stored in 'hutches' which survive above the harbour. The small breakwater pier was destroyed by storms in the early twentieth century, so that today only the foundations are seen at low tide amid scattered granite blocks.

BLUE HILLS TIN STREAMS
[SW 729516]
Trevellas Coombe was once busy with stamps and dressing floors all the way down to the beach. Today, a water-powered Cornish stamps and dressing plant produce small quantities of black tin for smelting on this site which is open to the public. Nearby, the old Blue Hills tin mine closed in 1897, after its last main working period of about 40 years. Remains include an engine house for a 70-inch pumping engine and the foundations of a horizontal single cylinder engine which drove stamps and a winder.

CLIGGA HEAD
[SW 738536]
High cliffs are honeycombed with mine workings southwards from Cligga Head to Hanover Cove, where green copper stains the rock. All this was part of the Perran St George Mine and Wheal Prudence, but most surface structures were demolished when the Perranporth airfield was built in the Second World War. Cligga Head itself was worked during the war for tin and wolfram

and has received attention in more recent years. There was also an explosives works here, of which several traces remain. There were other mines in the area. Wheal Leisure (1820-40) lay beneath Perranporth, then a mining and fishing village, and Droskyn Point has clear evidence of mining.

EAST WHEAL ROSE
[SW 839558]
In July 1846, a freak cloudburst caused the flooding of this rich lead and silver mine, and 38 miners were drowned in the worst disaster in a Cornish mine. In St Newlyn East churchyard a tombstone records one, Samuel May, aged 17. The mine was rich for another decade before output declined. During an attempt to revive the mine, a 100-inch pumping engine was set to work in 1884-5. It was the most powerful to be erected in Cornwall, but was widely travelled. Built by Harvey & Co. for Wheal Vor in 1853, the engine then served in North Wales before returning to East Wheal Rose in 1881; it finished its career at the Millom iron mines near Barrow. At East Wheal Rose, it was installed in the fine engine house which now stands as the centre-piece in the leisure park of the Lappa Valley Steam Railway.

GOONINNIS MINE
[SW 725503]
This was a trial mine, seeking tin on the south east side of St Agnes at the close of the nineteenth century, yet the remains are impressive. The 50-inch pumping engine house has a stack with a castellated top, as does the nearby whim boiler house.

GREAT PERRAN IRON LODE
[SW 764573 to SW 805554]
This iron lode can be seen exposed at the north end of Penhale Sands, and has been worked by mining and opencast methods for 2 1/2 miles [4 km] inland. In 1858-90 it produced 200,000 tons of iron ore and 32,000 tons of zinc blende. There was a great attempt to exploit the lode in the 1870s, when it was connected by the Cornwall Minerals Railway to the harbours at Newquay and Fowey. At Treamble, the lode was worked opencast in the late 1930s.

NORTH TRESKERBY MINE
[SW 723451]
North of the A30 near Scorrier is a good example of an engine house with a well proportioned chimney stack. This had an 80-inch pumping engine during a working of North Treskerby Mine in 1859-82, when mostly copper was produced.

POLBERRO MINE
[SW 717514]
This was once the richest tin mine in Cornwall. It was known as Royal Polberro Consols after Queen Victoria came here in 1846. Work ceased at the end of the nineteenth century, but Turnavore Shaft was re-opened in 1937-41, when it was deepened to 1,090 feet [332m]. The engine house at this shaft survives with a roof. Its 60-inch pumping engine was removed at the end of the nineteenth century to nearby Wheal Friendly, where it worked until 1918. The second house also remains [SW 720512], but is roofless.

TYWARNHAYLE MINES
[SW 701472]
This is one of Cornwall's most atmospheric mining landscapes when approached by a lane from Scorrier, down into the steep-sided valley which leads to the sea at Porthtowan. Standing high above is an engine house and stack at John's Shaft, where a 70-inch pumping engine worked for about ten years from 1860. Also known as Wheal Rock and United Hills, the mine was

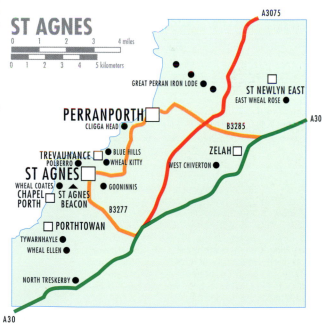

Wheal Coates M.J.M.

worked for copper in the nineteenth century. An attempt was made to reopen it in 1907. Wheal Ellen was another copper mine in the valley bottom, where there is an engine house with a fine castellated chimney stack [SW 703469]. Wheal Towan at Porthtowan was the most successful copper producer in the early nineteenth century, but little survives today.

WEST CHIVERTON MINE
[SW 791508]
This was a rich lead mine in the nineteenth century, producing silver and zinc ores too. 1,000 were employed at its busiest, and it closed in 1886. Surviving relics include the magnificent Batters' engine house, notable for the stack built in the centre of the back wall so that the cylinder arch had to be placed at one side. An 80-inch pumping engine worked here from 1869. It was built by Harvey & Co. and was said to be one of the finest engines made in Cornwall, later moving twice, to Gwennap United Mines and then to Great Condurrow.

WHEAL COATES
[SW 700502]
The engine house beside Towanroath Shaft is half way down the cliff in a much photographed situation between St Agnes Head and Chapel Porth. A 36-inch pumping engine was here in the 1870s, but a horizontal engine was installed during a later working. At low tide, the adit and lode can be seen from the beach at the foot of the cliff. On top of the cliff are the houses for winding and stamps engines. The mine never produced much tin or copper and closed in 1889, although an attempt was made again in about 1911. The engine houses have been restored by the National Trust.

WHEAL KITTY
[SW 725513]
This was the last tin mine to work in the district. It was combined with neighbouring Penhalls in a working of 1907-19, when a 65-inch pumping engine was erected in a house at Sara's Shaft. Further plant was installed when Wheal Kitty was re-opened in 1926, but it was short-lived, closing for ever in 1930. Remains include a horizontal winder house and boiler house.

ST AUSTELL DISTRICT

St Austell is best known for its china clay pits, but it was once important for mining too. North east of the town lay Carclaze, a huge opencast much visited by tourists in the eighteenth and nineteenth centuries. It was worked for tin and then china clay after about 1850. There were water powered stamping mills inside the pit, and access was through a canal tunnel. Important tin streamworks were on Redmoor, the Goss and Tregoss moors. There were deep alluvial deposits in the valley below Polgooth, where the Happy Union and Wheal Virgin works amalgamated to become the Pentewan Stream Mine. John Taylor was active in the district from the 1820s, at Charlestown United, Crinnis, Polgooth and Pembroke mines. Copper ores were shipped from Charlestown harbour, built in the 1790s, and Taylor had his own tin smelter there briefly in 1834-5.
The activities of Joseph Treffry (Austen until 1838) are better known. As a busy china clay port Par's origins are hardly recognisable today, but Treffry built the harbour after 1829 for shipping copper ores, and later granite and china clay from his mines and quarries. These were served by the Par Canal to Ponts Mill and then a tramway over a long incline and fine viaduct in the Luxulyan Valley. He also developed Newquay harbour and its tramway as an outlet for ores and clay on the north coast. The Cornwall Minerals Railway linked the two lines in 1874 by the section seen today on the Goss Moor parallel to the A30. There was a lead smelter at Par harbour until 1885. Its 235-foot [72m] high stack was a familiar landmark until it was demolished in 1907. William West's foundry at St Blazey made beam engines and other mining equipment from 1848 until 1891. The district has had a more recent history, in the shape of the Castle-an-Dinas wolfram in the first half of the twentieth century. On the south slope of the twin Belowda Beacon, the old Belowda Hill Mine has the first prominent engine house [SW 970622] to be seen when

entering Cornwall by the A30. North of St Austell, the Wheal Martyn China Clay Museum at Carthew [SX 005554] is worth visiting as it has some exhibits related to mining. There is a 35-foot [10.6m] waterwheel and another of 18 feet [5.5m] with flat rods, balance box and pump, and huge twin bore plunger pumps.

CASTLE-AN-DINAS MINE
[SW 945620]
Cornwall's most important wolfram mine was worked beneath Castle-an-Dinas hill from 1916 until 1957. The main North Shaft and mill were on the north side [SW 947628]. The South Shaft was sunk [SW 945620] in 1945 and some buildings, including those for the hoist and boiler house, survive here. The ore was sent to the mill by an aerial ropeway which passed through the Iron Age fort on the hilltop which is a landmark from the A30.

FOWEY CONSOLS
[SX 083560]
This great mine was developed after 1822 by J. T. Austen (later Treffry), becoming the largest copper mine east of St Day and employing nearly 2,000 persons. The mine was in profit until 1861, and closed down six years later after yielding 382,823 tons of copper ore.

In 1835, an 80-inch pumping engine was installed and trials showed this to be the finest ever built in Cornwall at the time. There were other engines, but much use was made of water power, with at least 13 waterwheels and three water pressure engines fed by water brought 4 miles [6.4 km] from Molinnis Moor in a leat

South Polgooth Mine P.S.

which crossed the Luxulyan valley by the Treffry Viaduct [SX 056572]. Other surface features included a clock tower, count house, saw mills, smithy, stables, a rope walk and, rare for a Cornish mine, barracks for some of the workers. Two inclined planes descended west down to the Par Canal which connected with Par harbour. The longest rose 280 feet [85m] to a point near Austen's engine house. The latter is the principal monument surviving, but the much quarried burrows to the south indicate the former extent of the mine.

GREAT POLGOOTH MINE
[SX 002506]
An important tin mine which had a smelting works before 1700. In 1727, Polgooth had one of only five recorded Newcomen engines in Cornwall. The last great working was from about 1820 when John Taylor took over. There were seven engines here, for pumping, winding and stamping. A prominent engine house stands on the St Austell golf course above Polgooth. The steep slope descending to the village has been ravaged by mining and at the bottom is a stamps engine house with a short chimney stack [SW 999505]. On the edge of

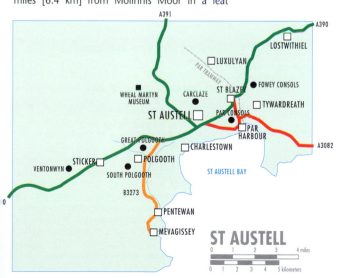

ST AUSTELL

Commerce Common to the south west is South Polgooth Mine [SW 990499] which was opened in the 1830s. Arsenic was produced when the mine last worked in 1916, and part of the calciner remains along with an earlier engine house.

PAR CONSOLS
[SX 072532]
Another rich copper mine opened by Treffry in 1840, with a direct inclined plane to Par harbour. Tin had become important by 1855. In 1863 there were at least 15 engines and nearly 500 persons employed. The mine closed four years later at a depth of 225 fathoms [411m]. Only a few traces remain.

RESTORMEL ROYAL IRON MINE
[SX 098612]
Open pits on the high ground between Lostwithiel and Restormel Castle are the only evidence of the largest iron mine in Cornwall. Levels were driven from the banks of the River Fowey and a tramway took ores to Lostwithiel to be barged down to Fowey harbour for shipment. The mine was managed by the Taylors, and Richard Taylor took Victoria and Albert around in 1846. Nearly 130,000 tons of iron ore were produced from 1855 until the mine's closure in 1883, but output varied drastically according to the price of iron.

VENTONWYN MINE
[SW 963504]
An engine house and its chimney stack stand alone in a field near Hewas Water, to the north of the A390 from which it is a conspicuous landmark. This was for a 36-inch rotative stamps engine. The mine last worked in 1903-7. A lone chimney stack to the north [SW 960509] was for a calciner on Great Dowgas Mine, and is interesting in that the stone masonry continues above the drip course instead of the more usual brick capping.

Ventonwyn Mine P.S.

The most extensive mining in the district took place around Caradon Hill on the edge of Bodmin Moor, where Minions village is the best centre for exploring the mines. There was earlier tin streaming and some mining, but the boom took off after a rich copper lode was discovered at South Caradon in 1836. The population was swelled by miners and their families who migrated from the west, and that of St Cleer parish had risen four-fold by 1861. The Liskeard & Caradon Railway was built in 1846 to Moorswater where ores were transferred to the Liskeard & Looe Union Canal for shipment from Looe. The railway was extended all the way in 1860. Exports at Looe also included granite and lead ores, while coal was imported for the engines on the mines. The upper part of the line around the Caradon mines became complex, and much can still be followed.

Lead mining was important in the Devonian rocks to west and east of Liskeard, at Herodsfoot and Menheniot. There were mines too around St Neot, and many small workings on and around the flanks of Bodmin Moor. Of these, the last was the Hawkswood wolfram mine near North Hill in the 1950s [SX 269756]. Most valleys and marshes on Bodmin Moor have been turned over for tin many times. Medieval streamworks and tin mills were investigated by archaeologists before the flooding of the Colliford Reservoir, but there are two areas of perhaps more recent date which are worth visiting. The first is in the north around Buttern Hill, and the second is in the south around Minions.

BUTTERN HILL STREAMWORKS
[SX 180823]
The valleys at the headwaters of Penpont Water have signs of extensive streamworking and openworks, particularly from Bowithick Marsh south towards Leskernick Hill. There was activity here in the early twentieth century, when a floating bucket dredger was tried at Bowithick with little success. At the same time, canvas pipes delivered water to hoses for washing out tin and wolfram ores on the side of Buttern Hill. The dam for this water can be seen at the edge of Kenniton Marsh [SX 168822], which was also worked for wolfram. This north part of Bodmin Moor has an interesting relic at Wheal Rosa [SX 157784], with the remains of a waterwheel and beam pumping mechanism for draining workings in Brown Willy Marsh.

HERODSFOOT MINE

[SX 212604 and SX 212600]

The hamlet of Herodsfoot in the West Looe valley is approached by steep lanes from all directions, and two groups of engine houses can be seen partly hidden by woodland. Lead was mined here in the eighteenth century, but the main workings began in about 1844 and soon there were over 200 miners aided by a 45-inch pumping engine, 22-inch winder and a waterwheel. In 1865 a larger 60-inch pumping engine replaced the old one. The mine reached 215 fathoms [393m] before most work ceased in 1884, although some continued until 1904. Output for 1848-84 was 19,010 tons of lead ore and 616,590 oz. of silver.

MARKE VALLEY MINE

[SX 277717]

The mine lies south of Upton Cross at the foot of Caradon Hill, and produced 128,500 tons of copper ore in 1844-90. The engine house at Salisbury Shaft has a striking cylinder arch, part of

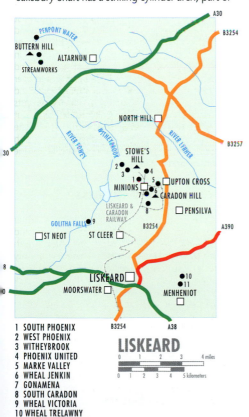

1 SOUTH PHOENIX
2 WEST PHOENIX
3 WITHEYBROOK
4 PHOENIX UNITED
5 MARKE VALLEY
6 WHEAL JENKIN
7 GONAMENA
8 SOUTH CARADON
9 WHEAL VICTORIA
10 WHEAL TRELAWNY
11 WHEAL MARY ANN

LISKEARD

a boiler house and a chimney. A 70-inch pumping engine was installed here in 1855. On the slope above, a winding engine house completes the scene. A branch from the Liskeard & Caradon Railway was built to the mine in 1877. The valley down from Minions and Wheal Jenkin once contained numerous stamping mills worked by waterwheels and one good example of a wheelpit survives.

PHOENIX UNITED MINE

[SX 267720]

This important mine was worked from 1844 to 1898, and produced over 82,000 tons of copper ore and 16,257 tons of black tin. There were a dozen engines for pumping, stamping and winding, but little remains. The count house is now a private residence. A wheelpit for a 60-foot [18.3m] diameter pumping wheel stands down in Clanacombe valley, which is also the site of streamworks treating the mineral-rich water discarded from the mine. A lode was worked westwards and a line of pits and collapsed shafts can be followed over the hill near Cheesewring Quarry to the demolished engine houses of West Phoenix Mine [SX 253721].

The most striking ruins are from 1907-14, when the Prince of Wales Shaft was sunk 1,193 feet [364m] in a failed attempt for tin. An 80-inch pumping engine built by Holman Bros. was installed in a large house, where it remained until about 1931. The impressive engine house has an unusual square-based chimney with a tall brick stack [SX 267720]. The boiler house is next door, and beside that are the house for a two-cylinder steam winder, its boiler house and a compressor house. Just to the east, a large building was for a Robey engine and its boilers for driving pneumatic stamps. The foundations overlook the site of the proposed dressing floors. A siding from the Liskeard & Caradon Railway is now a road track to the site.

SOUTH CARADON MINE

[SX 265700]

This great copper mine struck rich in 1836 in the Seaton valley just above Crow's Nest and its workings extend eastwards far under Caradon Hill. By 1865, 650 persons were employed. The mine closed in 1885 after producing 217,820 tons of ore, valued at £1,750,000. Dividends of £500,000 were paid on a capital outlay of only £640.

The main site has a cobbled ore floor, a reservoir and ruins of two drying houses and pumping engine houses [SX 265700]. Sump Shaft, the first above the valley floor, had a 50-inch

South Caradon Mine P.S.

pumping engine and reached 250 fathoms [457m]. Above the ruined engine house are houses for a whim engine and a second pumping engine. At Jope's Shaft [SX 265698], the 60-inch pumping engine house has a chimney and part of a boiler house. A man-engine was erected here in 1872. Eastwards, a group of engine houses at Rule's and Holman's Shafts [SX 269699] were part of the same mine, connected to the dressing floors by a tramway. Further east was Kittow's Shaft. Across the valley to the west was West Caradon Mine, working the same lode [SX 263700]. The huge burrows have been excavated for roadmaking, but the count house remains inhabited. There is little to see of East Caradon at Tokenbury Corner, a rich mine in 1860-85 [SX 279702].

SOUTH PHOENIX MINE
[SX 261715]
Worked on different occasions for copper and tin. A 50-inch pumping engine was installed in 1853 at Houseman's Shaft, and the bob wall of the tall engine house was later built up and the building converted to accommodation. It can be seen on the skyline from Dartmoor. Part of the engine house has been converted to a visitor centre for the Minions area. Just north is the collar of the inclined Parson's Shaft, while downslope are traces of dressing floors. Immediately behind Minions village are the concrete foundations of the last working of 1906-11 at Prosper Shaft.

WHEAL JENKIN
[SX 265712]
Two engine houses stand on each side of the Liskeard & Caradon Railway just east of Minions. The best preserved is the pumping engine house at Bellingham's Shaft, part of a late working for tin on this old mine by the Marke Valley company; a plaque inscribed 'M.V. 1886' records this. The 70-inch engine installed here had

previously worked on South Caradon Mine. The smaller house is more ruinous and was for a stamps engine. Dressing floors can be seen laid out on the slope below. The mine closed in 1890 after producing 292 tons of black tin.

WHEAL MARY ANN
[SX 288637]
A lead mine north of Menheniot beside the lane as it dips into a valley. It was named in 1843 after the wife of the Rev G. P. Norris, landowner of South Caradon Mine. In its time, the mine produced 29,600 tons of lead ore and 1,125,130 oz. of silver. It was abandoned in 1874 after an underground collapse, when the workings went down to 300 fathoms [548m], the deepest of any Cornish lead mine. Only six years before, a man-engine was installed for the 300 employees. There were seven steam engines and five waterwheels on the sett, yet little can be seen at the surface today. Wheal Trelawny and Wheal Hony were lead and silver mines worked at the same time just to the north, and a tall chimney stack with a decorated brick top survives at SX 288642.

WHEAL VICTORIA
[SX 224686]
Two large granite wheel pits are notable features beside the cascading River Fowey at Golitha Falls. At least one held a 30 x 7½ foot [9 x 2.3m] waterwheel which pumped from a shaft in the woods above via flat rods. A leat can be traced back upstream and there are several mine adits or

Houseman's Engine House, South Phoenix Mine P.S.

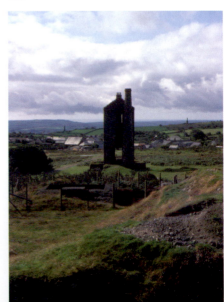

Wheal Jenkin P.S.

openings in the woods. The mine was tried for copper in the 1840s and 1850s.

WITHEYBROOK & GONAMENA STREAMWORKS
[SX 256719 & SX 265708]
Two sites, around Minions between Caradon Hill and the Cheesewring. The Witheybrook Streamwork is a deep and ancient openwork, dammed in the nineteenth century to provide water for West Phoenix Mine. There are signs of streamworks in the Witheybrook Marsh and further north down the valley. To south and west, streamworks and shallow workings continue down the valley towards Siblyback Reservoir. The Gonamena Streamwork is a huge excavation of several acres on the west slope of Caradon Hill. It was later worked by a level from the south end, where a finger-like projection is all that remains of an engine house on Gonamena Mine.

CALLINGTON DISTRICT

The area between Callington and Gunnislake, the latter with mine workings beneath the village itself. Ores were shipped from Calstock and Cotehele Quays on the Tamar, carried down by road until the East Cornwall Mineral Railway was opened in 1872. The line was 7 1/2 miles [12 km] from Kelly Bray, descending to Calstock Quay by an incline. The 3ft 6ins [1.06m] gauge track, was relaid to standard gauge when the Calstock viaduct was opened across the Tamar in 1908, but most mining activity had ceased by then. The mineralised zone continues across the Tamar

into Devon, where Devon Great Consols was the richest copper mine in Europe and had its own mineral line to Morwellham Quay, now a tourist attraction.

DRAKEWALLS MINE
[SX 425706]
Ruined engine houses and chimneys can be seen from the A390 almost at the top of the hill as it climbs from Gunnislake. Drakewalls was an important tin mine, worked in the eighteenth century by a long deep opening or gunnis. In 1859 it was the largest tin mine in east Cornwall, employing nearly 400. Over 5,000 tons of black tin were produced before the end of the century, although arsenic became more important after 1888. The Oxland process for separating wolfram from tin was first used here. Drakewalls was drained by a deep adit from near the Tamar, and was last worked in 1900-10.

GREENHILL ARSENIC WORKS
[SX 418717]
A huge but damaged chimney stack dominates the hill above Gunnislake and can be seen from Plymouth. It was built in 1894 as part of the Greenhill Arsenic Works, where arsenic was refined to the highest grades. The twin sites included a cooperage to make arsenic barrels, and tin smelting and brick making works, connected by an incline.

HINGSTON DOWN CONSOLS
[SX 409715]
There were early workings for tin on top of Hingston Down, but a copper mine worked in 1850-78. It was re-opened for tin in 1905-8 with Gunnislake Clitters mine. There is a curious engine house here with its roof hidden by a parapet. It contained a rotative beam engine for winding and pumping via flat rods at Bailey's Shaft just to the south. Hingston Down Quarry encroaches on the north side.

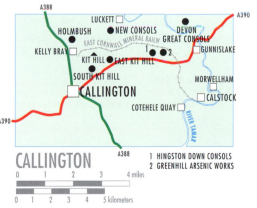

CALLINGTON

1 HINGSTON DOWN CONSOLS
2 GREENHILL ARSENIC WORKS

0   1   2   3   4 miles

0 1 2 3 4   5 kilometers

49

Holmbush Mine P.S.

HOLMBUSH MINE

[SX 358721]

Three engine houses can be seen at the edge of a wood between the fork of the Launceston and Stoke Climsland roads, north of Kelly Bray. This was Holmbush Mine, worked to a depth of 217 fathoms [397m] from the 1830s, when over 200 were employed. Copper and some lead were produced, and the dumps indicate iron ores too. South of Kelly Bray is Redmoor Mine [SX 356710], from which copper and lead blocks of over a ton each were raised for the Great Exhibition of 1851. In the early 1980s, this was the proposed site for the South West Consolidated tin mine, now abandoned.

KIT HILL MINES

[SX 375713]

Much of the hill, now the Kit Hill Country Park, is pitted with workings and shafts which date back a long way. The summit is a fine viewpoint, and has a monumental chimney stack [SX 375713] built in 1858 for Kithill Consols. It is over 80 feet [24m] high and served a 30-inch winding and stamping engine in a house nearby. In the 1830s, there had been a wind engine on Kit Hill Mine. The stack of South Kithill Mine [SX 374709] is seen silhouetted on the slope of Kit Hill when entering Cornwall by the A390 from the Gunnislake border crossing. This was a small tin mine, worked in 1870-83. An engine house of East Kithill Mine is close to the A390 at SX 389711. Ore from Kithill Mine was stamped and dressed here early in the twentieth century.

NEW CONSOLS MINE

[SX 387736]

At Luckett near the banks of the Tamar was Wheal Martha, first worked for copper and some tin. It became New Consols in 1867-79, with five steam engines for pumping, winding, stamping and crushing, supplemented by three large waterwheels. A fine collection of engines remained in their houses from 1879 until they were broken up in the Second World War. The empty engine houses survive, two with their slate roofs. Arsenic was important and a long flue was built from the calciners to a stack beside the road up the hill towards Monkscross. New Consols last worked in 1946-52, when tin dressing mills were erected.

East Kit Hill level M.J.M.